Kyle Baker

NAT TURNER

KYLE BAKER PUBLISHING

NEW YORK

NAT TURNER ENCORE EDITON VOL. 1 OF 2

Published by

KYLE BAKER PUBLISHING

368 BROADWAY STE 315

NEW YORK, NY 10013

VISIT WWW.KYLEBAKER.COM

ISBN: 0-9747214-2-5

ISBN 13: 978-0-9747214-2-2

FIRST PRINTING 2006

10 9 8 7 6 5 4 3 2 1

Printed in Canada

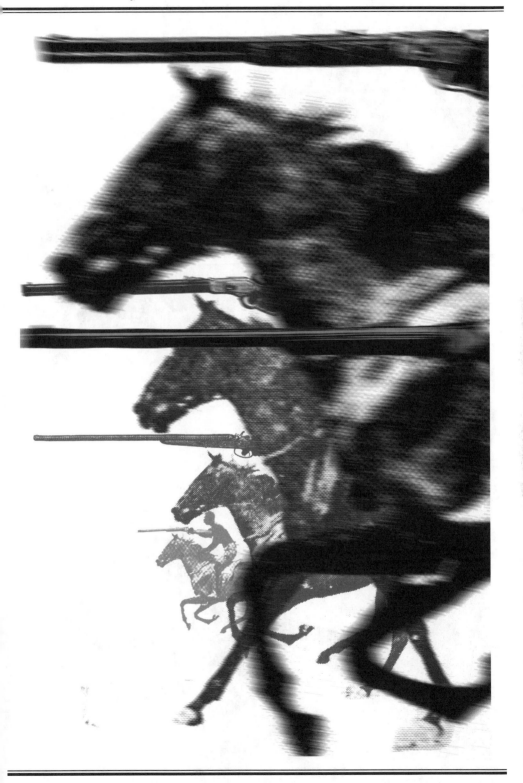

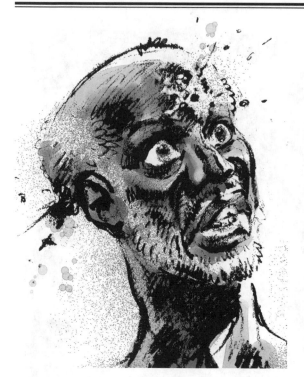

BOOM!

BOOM!

BOOM!

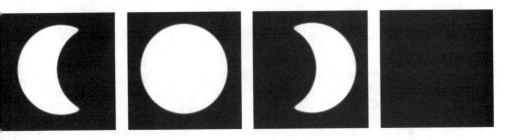

FROM THE MEMOIRS OF CAPTAIN THEODORE CANOT, *TWENTY YEARS OF AN AFRICAN SLAVER*

"*T*HE HEAD OF EVERY MALE AND FEMALE IS NEATLY SHAVED; AND, IF THE CARGO BELONGS TO SEVERAL OWNERS, EACH MAN'S BRAND IS IMPRESSED ON THE BODY OF HIS RESPECTIVE NEGRO. [...] THEY ARE ENTIRELY STRIPPED, SO THAT WOMEN AS WELL AS MEN GO OUT OF AFRICA AS THEY CAME INTO IT--NAKED.

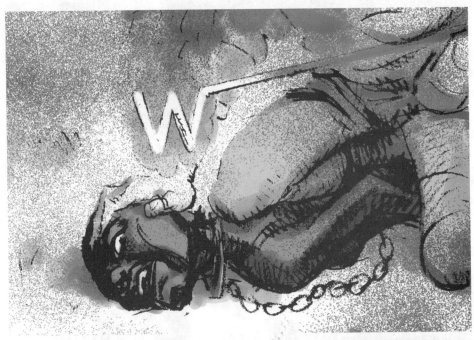

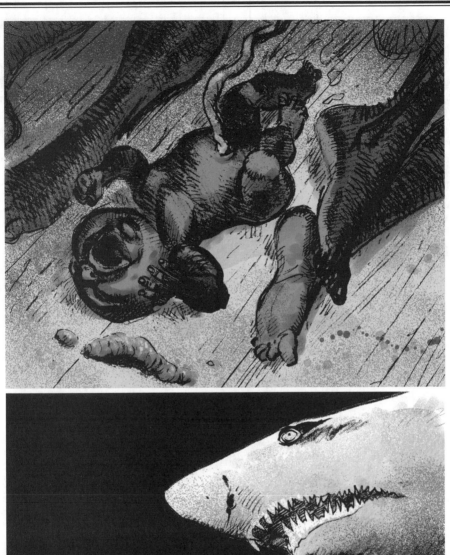

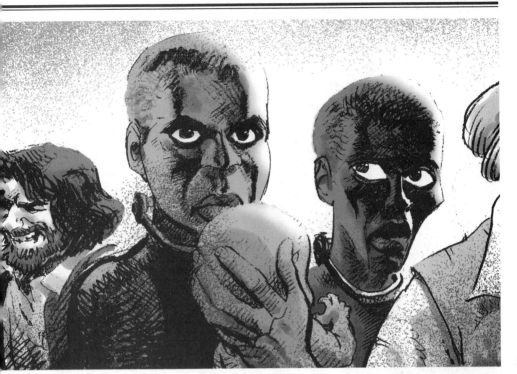

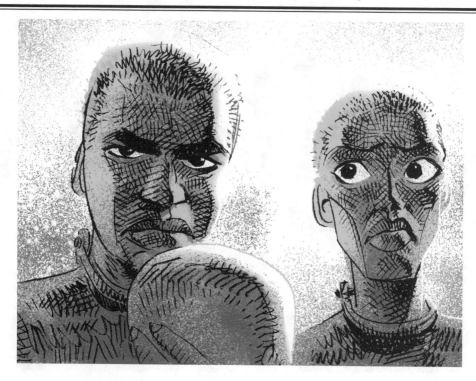

FROM THE CONFESSION OF NAT TURNER

"IT IS HERE NECESSARY TO RELATE THIS CIRCUMSTANCE - TRIFLING AS IT MAY SEEM, IT WAS THE COMMENCEMENT OF THAT BELIEF WHICH HAS GROWN WITH TIME, AND EVEN NOW SIR, IN THIS DUNGEON, HELPLESS AND FORSAKEN AS I AM, I CANNOT DIVEST MYSELF OF IT. BEING AT PLAY WITH OTHER CHILDREN, WHEN THREE OR FOUR YEARS OLD, I WAS TELLING THEM SOMETHING, WHICH MY MOTHER OVERHEARING, SAID IT HAD HAPPENED BEFORE I WAS BORN - I STUCK TO MY STORY, HOWEVER, AND RELATED SOME THINGS WHICH WENT, IN HER OPINION, TO CONFIRM IT - OTHERS BEING CALLED ON WERE GREATLY ASTONISHED, KNOWING THAT THESE THINGS HAD HAPPENED, AND CAUSED THEM TO SAY IN MY HEARING, I SURELY WOULD BE A PROPHET, AS THE LORD HAD SHEWN ME THINGS THAT HAD HAPPENED BEFORE MY BIRTH."

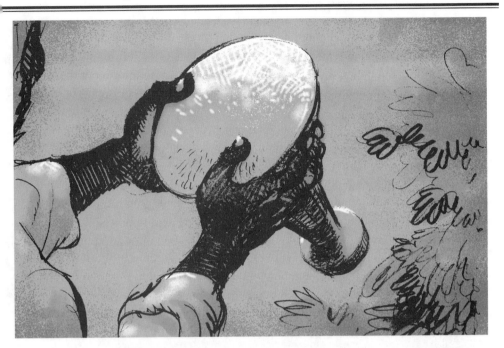

BOOM
B-B-BOOM
B-B-BOOM
BOOM
BOOM
B-BOOM

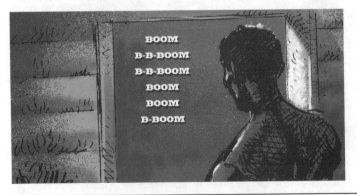

BOOM B-B-BOOM
B-B-BOOM BOOM
BOOM B-BOOM

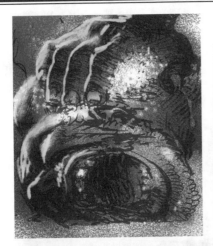

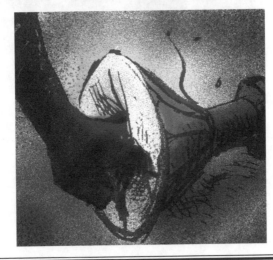

FROM THE CONFESSIONS OF NAT TURNER:

"My father and mother strengthened me in this my first impression, saying in my presence, I was intended for some great purpose, which they had always thought from certain marks on my head and breast. My grandmother, who was very religious, and to whom I was much attached - my master, who belonged to the church, and other religious persons who visited the house, and whom I often saw at prayers, noticing the singularity of my manners, I suppose, and my uncommon intelligence for a child, remarked I had too much sense to be raised, and if I was, I would never be of any service to any one as a slave

SLAM.

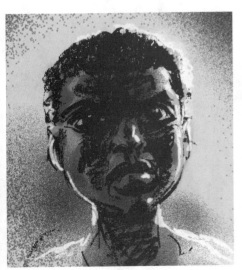

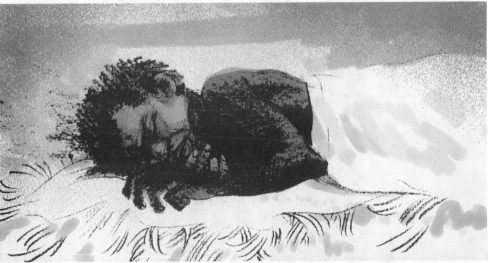

"TO A MIND LIKE MINE, RESTLESS, INQUISITIVE AND OBSERVANT OF EVERY THING THAT WAS PASSING, IT IS EASY TO SUPPOSE THAT RELIGION WAS THE SUBJECT TO WHICH IT WOULD BE DIRECTED, AND ALTHOUGH THIS SUBJECT PRINCIPALLY OCCUPIED MY THOUGHTS - THERE WAS NOTHING THAT I SAW OR HEARD OF TO WHICH MY ATTENTION WAS NOT DIRECTED

"*T*HE MANNER IN WHICH I LEARNED TO READ AND WRITE, NOT ONLY HAD GREAT INFLUENCE ON MY OWN MIND, AS I ACQUIRED IT WITH THE MOST PERFECT EASE, SO MUCH SO, THAT I HAVE NO RECOLLECTION WHATEVER OF LEARNING THE ALPHABET -

"*B*UT TO THE ASTONISHMENT OF THE FAMILY, ONE DAY WHEN A BOOK WAS SHEWN TO ME TO KEEP ME FROM CRYING , I BEGAN SPELLING THE NAMES OF DIFFERENT OBJECTS

"THIS WAS A SOURCE OF WONDER TO ALL IN THE NEIGHBORHOOD, PARTICULARLY THE BLACKS - AND THIS LEARNING WAS CONSTANTLY IMPROVED AT ALL OPPORTUNITIES

"WHEN I GOT LARGE ENOUGH TO GO TO WORK, WHILE EMPLOYED, I WAS REFLECTING ON MANY THINGS THAT WOULD PRESENT THEMSELVES TO MY IMAGINATION, AND WHENEVER AN OPPORTUNITY OCCURRED OF LOOKING AT A BOOK, WHEN THE SCHOOL CHILDREN WERE GETTING THEIR LESSONS, I WOULD FIND MANY THINGS THAT THE FERTILITY OF MY OWN IMAGINATION HAD DEPICTED TO ME BEFORE; ALL MY TIME, NOT DEVOTED TO MY MASTER'S SERVICE, WAS SPENT EITHER IN PRAYER, OR IN MAKING EXPERIMENTS IN CASTING DIFFERENT THINGS IN MOLDS MAKE OF EARTH, IN ATTEMPTING TO MAKE PAPER, GUN-POWDER AND MANY OTHER EXPERIMENTS, THAT ALTHOUGH I COULD NOT PERFECT, YET CONVINCED ME OF ITS PRACTICABILITY IF I HAD THE MEANS.

"I WAS NOT ADDICTED TO STEALING IN MY YOUTH, NOR HAVE EVER BEEN - YET SUCH WAS THE CONFIDENCE OF THE NEGROES IN THE NEIGHBORHOOD, EVEN AT THIS EARLY PERIOD OF MY LIFE, IN MY SUPERIOR JUDGMENT, THAT THEY WOULD OFTEN CARRY ME WITH THEM WHEN THEY WERE GOING ON ANY ROGUERY, TO PLAN FOR THEM.

"GROWING UP AMONG THEM WITH THIS CONFIDENCE IN MY SUPERIOR JUDGMENT, AND WHEN THIS, IN THEIR OPINIONS, WAS PERFECTED BY DIVINE INSPIRATION, FROM THE CIRCUMSTANCES ALREADY ALLUDED TO IN MY INFANCY, AND WHICH BELIEF WAS EVER AFTERWARDS ZEALOUSLY INCULCATED BY THE AUSTERITY OF MY LIFE AND MANNERS, WHICH BECAME THE SUBJECT OF REMARK BY WHITE AND BLACK.

"HAVING SOON DISCOVERED TO BE GREAT, I MUST APPEAR SO, AND THEREFORE STUDIOUSLY AVOIDED MIXING IN SOCIETY, AND WRAPPED MYSELF IN MYSTERY, DEVOTING MY TIME TO FASTING AND PRAYER.

"By this time having arrived to man's estate, and hearing the scriptures commented on at meetings, I was struck with that particular passage which says: "Seek ye the kingdom of Heaven and all things shall be added unto you." I reflected much on this passage, and prayed daily for light on this subject - As I was praying one day at my plough, the Spirit spoke to me, saying "Seek ye the kingdom of Heaven and all things shall be added unto you." Question - what do you mean by the Spirit. Ans. The Spirit that spoke to the prophets in former days - and I was greatly astonished, and for two years prayed continually, whenever my duty would permit - and then again I had the same revelation, which fully confirmed me in the impression that I was ordained for some great purpose in the hands of the Almighty. Several years rolled round, in which many events occurred to strengthen me in this my belief. At this time I reverted in my mind to the remarks made of me in my childhood, and the things that had been shewn me - and as it had been said of me in my childhood by those by whom I had been taught to pray, both white and black, and in whom I had the greatest confidence, that I had too much sense to be raised, and if I was, I would never be of any use to any one as a slave. Now finding I had arrived to man's estate, and was a slave, and these revelations being made known to me, I began to direct my attention to this great object, to fulfill the purpose for which, by this time, I felt assured I was intended.

"**K**NOWING THE INFLUENCE I HAD OBTAINED OVER THE MINDS OF MY FELLOW SERVANTS, (NOT BY THE MEANS OF CONJURING AND SUCH LIKE TRICKS - FOR TO THEM I ALWAYS SPOKE OF SUCH THINGS WITH CONTEMPT) BUT BY THE COMMUNION OF THE SPIRIT WHOSE REVELATIONS I OFTEN COMMUNICATED TO THEM, AND THEY BELIEVED AND SAID MY WISDOM CAME FROM GOD. I NOW BEGAN TO PREPARE THEM FOR MY PURPOSE, BY TELLING THEM SOMETHING WAS ABOUT TO HAPPEN THAT WOULD TERMINATE IN FULFILLING THE GREAT PROMISE THAT HAD BEEN MADE TO ME ∽

"ABOUT THIS TIME I WAS PLACED UNDER AN OVERSEER, FROM WHOM I RAN AWAY

"After remaining in the woods thirty days, I returned, to the astonishment of the Negroes on the plantation, who thought I had made my escape to some other part of the country, as my father had done before. But the reason of my return was, that the Spirit appeared to me and said I had my wishes directed to the things of this world, and not to the kingdom of Heaven, and that I should return to the service of my earthly master - "For he who knoweth his Master's will, and doeth it not, shall be beaten with many stripes, and thus have I chastened you." And the Negroes found fault, and murmured against me, saying that if they had my sense they would not serve any master in the world.

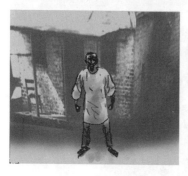

"_A_ND ABOUT THIS TIME I HAD A VISION - AND I SAW WHITE SPIRITS AND BLACK SPIRITS ENGAGED IN BATTLE, AND THE SUN WAS DARKENED - THE THUNDER ROLLED IN THE HEAVENS, AND BLOOD FLOWED IN STREAMS AND I HEARD A VOICE SAYING, "SUCH IS YOUR LUCK, SUCH YOU ARE CALLED TO SEE, AND LET IT COME ROUGH OR SMOOTH, YOU MUST SURELY BARE IT. I NOW WITHDREW MYSELF AS MUCH AS MY SITUATION WOULD PERMIT, FROM THE INTERCOURSE OF MY FELLOW SERVANTS, FOR THE AVOWED PURPOSE OF SERVING THE SPIRIT MORE FULLY - AND IT APPEARED TO ME, AND REMINDED ME OF THE THINGS IT HAD ALREADY SHOWN ME, AND THAT IT WOULD THEN REVEAL TO ME THE KNOWLEDGE OF THE ELEMENTS, THE REVOLUTION OF THE PLANETS, THE OPERATION OF TIDES, AND CHANGES OF THE SEASONS. AFTER THIS REVELATION IN THE YEAR OF 1825, AND THE KNOWLEDGE OF THE ELEMENTS BEING MADE KNOWN TO ME, I SOUGHT MORE THAN EVER TO OBTAIN TRUE HOLINESS BEFORE THE GREAT DAY OF JUDGMENT SHOULD APPEAR, AND

THEN I BEGAN TO RECEIVE THE TRUE KNOWLEDGE OF FAITH. AND FROM THE FIRST STEPS OF RIGHTEOUSNESS UNTIL THE LAST, WAS I MADE PERFECT; AND THE HOLY GHOST WAS WITH ME, AND SAID, "BEHOLD ME AS I STAND IN THE HEAVENS" - AND I LOOKED AND SAW THE FORMS OF MEN IN DIFFERENT ATTITUDES - AND THERE WERE LIGHTS IN THE SKY TO WHICH THE CHILDREN OF DARKNESS GAVE OTHER NAMES THAN WHAT THEY REALLY WERE- FOR THEY WERE THE LIGHTS OF THE SAVIOR'S HANDS, STRETCHED FORTH FROM EAST TO WEST, EVEN AS THEY WERE EXTENDED ON THE CROSS ON CALVARY FOR THE REDEMPTION OF SINNERS. AND I WONDERED GREATLY AT THESE MIRACLES, AND PRAYED TO BE INFORMED OF A CERTAINTY OF THE MEANING THEREOF - AND SHORTLY AFTERWARDS, WHILE LABORING IN THE FIELD, I DISCOVERED DROPS OF BLOOD ON THE CORN AS THOUGH IT WERE DEW FROM HEAVEN - AND I COMMUNICATED IT TO MANY, BOTH WHITE AND BLACK, IN THE NEIGHBORHOOD

"*A*ND ON THE 12TH OF MAY, 1828, I HEARD A LOUD NOISE IN THE HEAVENS, AND THE SPIRIT INSTANTLY APPEARED TO ME AND SAID THE SERPENT WAS LOOSENED, AND CHRIST HAD LAID DOWN THE YOKE HE HAD BORNE FOR THE SINS OF MEN, AND THAT I SHOULD TAKE IT ON AND FIGHT AGAINST THE SERPENT, FOR THE TIME WAS FAST APPROACHING WHEN THE FIRST SHOULD BE LAST AND THE LAST SHOULD BE FIRST."

To Be Continued

Bibliography

Ploski, Harry A. (Editor) *Reference Library Of Black America* Afro-American Press

Gray, Thomas *The Confessions Of Nat Turner*

Oates, Stephen B. *The Fires Of Jubilee: Nat Turner's Fierce Rebellion* Harper Collins

Bisson, Terry *Nat Turner: Slave Revolt Leader* Grolier Inc.

Canot, Theodore, Capt. *Adventures Of An American Slaver* Dover Publications

Bok, Francis *Escape From Slavery* St. Martin's Press

Thomas, Velma Maia *Lest We Forget* Crown Publishing Group

Library Of Congress Slave Narrative Collection http://memory.loc.gov:8081/ammem/snhtml/snhome.html

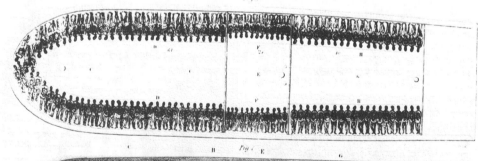

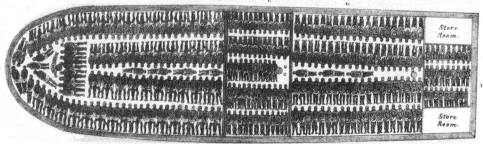

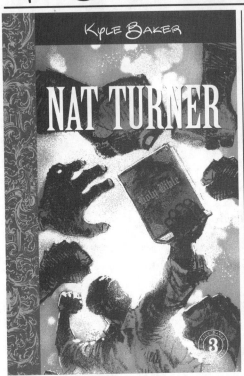